The Masked Cleaning Ladies of Om

Dramatised from
John Coldwell's stor
by David Calcutt

Illustrated by Joseph Sharples

Oxford University Press

Oxford University Press, Great Clarendon Street, Oxford OX2 6DP

Oxford New York
Athens Auckland Bangkok Bogota Buenos Aires Calcutta
Cape Town Chennai Dar es Salaam Delhi Florence Hong Kong
Istanbul Karachi Kuala Lumpur Madrid Melbourne Mexico City
Mumbai Nairobi Paris São Paulo Singapore Taipei Tokyo
Toronto Warsaw

and associated companies in
Berlin Ibadan

Oxford is a trade mark of Oxford University Press

© David Calcutt 1998

First published 1998

Adapted from the novel **The Masked Cleaning Ladies of Om** by John Coldwell, published by Oxford University Press in 1995

ISBN 0 19 918780 0

All rights reserved. This publication may not be reproduced, stored in a retrieval system, or transmitted, in any form or by any means, without the prior permission in writing of Oxford University Press. Within the UK, exceptions are allowed in respect of any fair dealing for the purpose of research or private study, or criticism or review, as permitted under the Copyright, Designs and Patents Act, 1988 or in the case of reprographic reproduction in accordance with the terms of licences issued by the Copyright Licensing Agency. Enquiries concerning reproduction outside those terms and in other countries should be sent to the Rights Department, Oxford University Press, at the address above.

All applications for public performance of this adaptation should be addressed in the first instance to the Permissions Controller, Educational Division, Oxford University Press, Great Clarendon Street, Oxford OX2 6DP.

Designed by Holbrook Design (Oxford) Limited

Printed in Hong Kong

Cast list

Mrs Binns

Queen Norah

King Harry

Princess Jane

Captain Smith

Captain Jones

Mary

The roles of Mrs Binns and Mary can be played by the same actor.

The play is set in the castle belonging to Queen Norah and King Harry.

Scene 1

A room in the castle. There is a mess on the floor – toys and books and games are scattered everywhere. ***Mrs Binns*** *enters and looks at the mess. She is angry.*

Mrs Binns *(To herself)* Look at this awful mess! I give up! *(She calls out)* Queen Norah! Queen Norah!

Queen Norah *enters.*

Queen Norah Yes, Mrs Binns?

Mrs Binns I've had enough!

Queen Norah Had enough? What do you mean?

Mrs Binns All this mess! I can't clear it up. It's too much work for one person to do. And I won't do it any more.

Queen Norah *(Shocked)* But you're our cleaning lady. You're our royal cleaning lady!

Mrs Binns Not any more, I'm not. I'm leaving.

Queen Norah You can't.

Mrs Binns I can, and I will. Goodbye.

***Mrs Binns** turns and starts to walk off.*
***Queen Norah** calls after her.*

Queen Norah But who's going to clean the castle from now on?

***Mrs Binns** stops and turns back to her.*

Mrs Binns I don't know. You'll have to find somebody else.
If you can.

***Mrs Binns** goes. **Queen Norah** looks around at all the mess. She speaks to herself, and gets more and more upset.*

Queen Norah Oh, dear. Oh, dear, oh, dear. This is terrible.
This is awful! Oh, dear, oh, dear, oh, dear!

***Queen Norah** goes off.*

Scene 2

Another room in the castle. ***Princess Jane*** *is playing on the floor.* ***King Harry*** *is reading his newspaper.* ***Queen Norah*** *enters, in a bad mood.*

King Harry Norah? What's the matter? You look upset.

Queen Norah I am. I'm very upset.

King Harry Why? What's happened?

Queen Norah Mrs Binns has left us.

King Harry *(Shocked)* Left us?

Queen Norah Yes. She's gone.

King Harry Gone? Mrs Binns?

Queen Norah Yes! She's gone, and she's left us with all this mess!

King Harry I can see why you're upset. This is bad news. Oh, dear. Oh, dear. Oh, dear, oh, dear, oh, dear. This is a problem. We shall have to think what to do.

Jane Mum! Can Mary come round to play?

Queen Norah No, she can't.

***Jane** is shocked by her answer.*

Jane Why not?

Queen Norah Because when your friends come round they make too much mess!

Jane I know. But Mrs Binns always clears it up.

Queen Norah	She won't any more. So, from now on, I'm afraid none of your friends can come round to play.
Jane	*(Upset)* But, Mum – !
Queen Norah	*(Strictly)* That's enough, Jane! Remember you're a princess. Princesses don't moan!

***King Harry** looks up from his thoughts.*

King Harry	I've had an idea.
Queen Norah	Oh, good. What is it?
King Harry	*We* can keep the castle tidy.

Queen Norah	What? You mean us?
King Harry	Yes. I can do a bit of washing. And I'm sure Captain Jones and Captain Smith will help as well.
Queen Norah	No! That won't do! We are a royal family! We can't have people saying that King Harry does his own cleaning! No! Never!
King Harry	It was just a thought.
Queen Norah	And it wasn't a very good one.
Jane	I've got an idea...
Queen Norah	I hope it's better than your father's.
Jane	We can put up an advert for a new cleaner.
Queen Norah	An advert. That *is* a good idea, Jane.
Jane	It can say, 'Cleaner wanted. Good pay. Ask at the Castle.'

Queen Norah Very good. Go and write it straight away and pin it to the castle door.

Jane *(Excited)* I will!

She goes. ***Queen Norah*** *speaks to King Harry.*

Queen Norah Come on, King Harry. Let's get away from this mess. I'm sure it won't be long before we have a new cleaner, and it's all tidied away.

King Harry I hope you're right, dear.

Queen Norah Of course I am. I'm always right.

Queen Norah *and* ***King Harry*** *go.*

Scene 3

The same room in the castle a few days later. The mess is still on the floor. ***Captain Smith*** *enters from one side of the stage, and* ***Captain Jones*** *enters from the other side.*

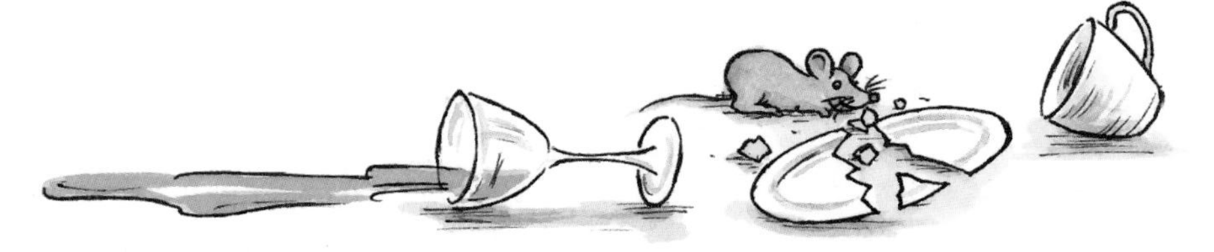

Captain Smith Good morning, Captain Jones.

Captain Jones Good morning, Captain Smith.

Captain Smith The place is still a mess, I see.

Captain Jones I'm afraid it is.

Captain Smith They've had no luck with finding a new cleaner?

Captain Jones None at all. The notice has been on the castle door for days, but no one's been to ask about it.

Captain Smith And the castle is getting messier.

Captain Jones And dirtier.

Captain Smith And filthier.

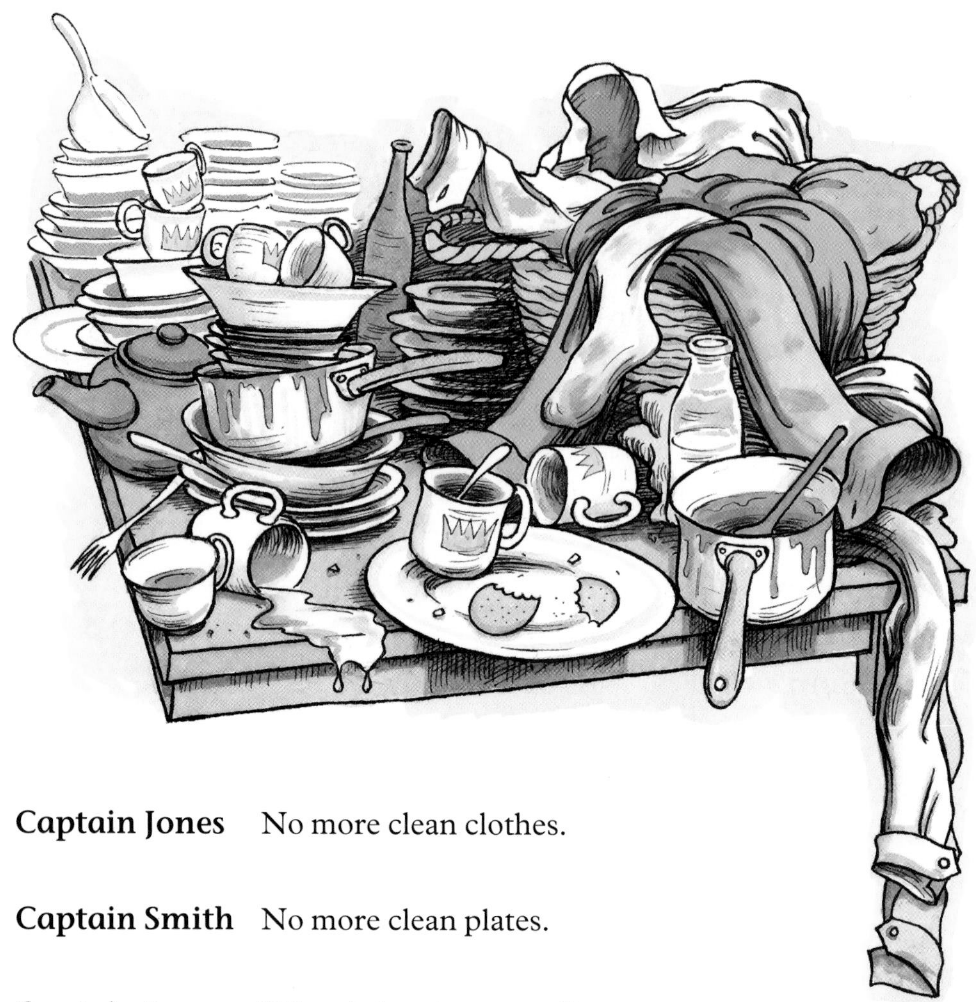

Captain Jones No more clean clothes.

Captain Smith No more clean plates.

Captain Jones Where's it going to end?

Captain Smith And what's going to be done about it?

***King Harry** enters. He carries a pair of rubber gloves, a mop, and some dirty laundry.*

King Harry I'll tell you what's going to be done about it. We're going to clean it up, that's what.

Captain Jones That's just what I was going to say myself, Your Majesty.

Captain Smith If we don't, who will?

King Harry I'm glad you agree. I can't stand this mess any longer. Let's start work straight away.

He gives the dirty laundry to Captain Jones.

King Harry You can put these in the washing machine.

Captain Jones Good. I love the smell of washing powder!

***King Harry** gives the mop to Captain Smith.*

King Harry You can mop.

Captain Smith Mopping's my favourite.

King Harry And I'll get on with the washing up.

King Harry *puts on the rubber gloves, goes off, and returns with a bowl of cups and plates and a small washing-up mop. He begins to wipe the plates with the mop. At the same time,* ***Captain Jones*** *sorts out the shirts, and* ***Captain Smith*** *mops the floor. They hum a happy tune as they work.* ***Jane*** *enters.*

Jane	Father? What are you doing?
King Harry	Jane, my dear. Just in time. You can help as well.
Jane	*(Worried)* But Father –
King Harry	Don't just stand there. You can help Captain Jones with the laundry.

***Jane** sighs, then starts to help. But a few seconds later, **Queen Norah** enters. She sees what they are doing and cries out in horror.*

Queen Norah What on earth do you think you're doing?

__King Harry__ jumps when he hears Queen Norah.

King Harry My dear! We're just… tidying things up a little –

Queen Norah I can see that! Stop it! Stop it at once! Jane! Captain Jones! Put down those shirts!

***Jane** and **Captain Jones** drop the laundry.*

Queen Norah Captain Smith! Drop that mop!

***Captain Smith** lets the mop fall.*

Queen Norah And you, King Harry! Take off those rubber gloves immediately!

King Harry But, my dear – !

Queen Norah Do as you're told!

King Harry Yes, dear.

***King Harry** takes off the gloves.*

Queen Norah You should all be ashamed of yourselves. I've never seen anything so shocking in all my life. Sweeping and mopping and tidying up. These are not jobs for a king and his captains! You should be out fighting dragons!

Captain Jones *(To Captain Smith)* Did she say 'dragons'?

Captain Smith *(To Captain Jones)* I think so.

Queen Norah Yes, I did. That's what you should be doing. Fighting dragons.

King Harry But we've never seen any dragons, dear.

Queen Norah Have you looked for them?

King Harry No.

Queen Norah There you are, then. You won't find them unless you go looking for them. And that's just what you're going to do.

***Captain Jones, Captain Smith**, and **King Harry** all speak together.*

All What!

Queen Norah You're going on a quest to find a dragon.

Captain Jones And what do we do when we find one, Your Majesty?

Captain Smith *If* we find one?

Queen Norah Fight it, of course! And while you're about it, you can look out for a cleaner as well. I shall expect to see her here at work when I get back.

King Harry When you get back? Are you going somewhere?

Queen Norah Yes. I am going on a Royal Tour.

King Harry When?

Queen Norah Just as soon as you three have gone off on your quest.

Captain Jones To find a dragon.

Captain Smith And a cleaner.

Queen Norah	That's right. Well? What are you waiting for? Off you go.
King Harry	*(Unhappily)* Yes, dear. Goodbye.
Queen Norah	Goodbye.
King Harry	Goodbye, Jane.
Jane	Goodbye, Dad. And good luck.
King Harry	Thank you. I think we're going to need it. *(He speaks to the Captains)* Captain Smith, Captain Jones. Lead on.

***Captain Jones*, *Captain Smith*, and *King Harry* go. *Jane* waves sadly after them.**

Queen Norah Good. Now I can go off on my Royal Tour.

Jane What about me? What am I going to do?

Queen Norah You can stay here and look after the castle. And don't let any burglars in. Or your friends. Goodbye.

***Queen Norah* goes. *Jane* sits down on the floor, puts her head in her hands, and sulks.**

Scene 4

The same as the end of Scene 3. ***Jane*** *is sitting sulking on the floor. Her friend,* ***Mary****, enters.*

Mary Jane?

Jane *looks round, surprised.*

Jane Mary! What are you doing here?

Mary I came to see you.

Jane How did you get in?

Mary The footman let me in. You look fed up.

Jane I am. Mum's gone off on a tour, and Dad's gone off on a quest, and I'm stuck here alone in this smelly old castle. And it's not fair!

Mary You're not alone now. I'm here.

Jane I know. But as soon as Mum comes back she'll send you away.

Mary Why?

Jane I'm not allowed to have any friends round. She said they make too much mess.

Mary Haven't you got a cleaner?

Jane No. She left.

Mary Clean things up yourself, then. I'll help.

Jane There's too much to do. The whole place is filthy. Anyway, we're not allowed to clean because we're a Royal Family. Sometimes it's not much fun being a princess.

Mary Isn't there anything I can do?

Jane Yes. You can sit down here and sulk with me.

__Mary__ sits next to Jane. They sulk together. Behind them, __Captain Jones__ enters. He is wearing an apron, rubber gloves, and a mask over his head.

Captain Jones Don't cry!

__Captain Smith__ enters, wearing a dress, rubber gloves, and a mask over his head.

Captain Smith Don't sulk!

King Harry *enters, wearing a pinafore, rubber gloves, and a mask over his head.*

King Harry Don't be sad!

Captain Jones The cleaners are here –

Captain Smith To bring you good cheer –

King Harry And make you happy and glad!

Jane *and* ***Mary*** *both jump to their feet, very surprised.*

Jane Who are you?

Captain Jones We are the Masked Cleaning Ladies of Om.

Captain Smith Your father sent us here.

Jane That was quick. Where is my father?

King Harry Chasing dragons.

Mary Why are you wearing masks?

Captain Jones	To protect ourselves from the dust.
Captain Smith	And there seems to be a lot of dust here.
King Harry	And a lot of mess.
Captain Jones	The whole place is filthy.
Captain Smith	It looks like we got here just in time.
King Harry	When can we start?
Jane	Straight away. Here's a dustpan and brush.

Captain Jones I'll take those.

***Jane** gives the dustpan and brush to Captain Jones.*

Mary There's a mop and bucket here.

Captain Smith And I'll have those.

***Mary** gives the mop and bucket to Captain Smith.*

Jane And here's a vacuum cleaner.

King Harry That's for me. Thank you.

***Jane** gives the vacuum cleaner to King Harry. **King Harry** speaks to the two captains.*

King Harry Well, ladies? Where shall we begin?

Captain Jones Upstairs, I think.

Captain Smith Then we can work our way down.

King Harry Good idea. *(He speaks to Jane and Mary)* Just leave everything to us. We'll soon have the whole place cleaned up.

Captain Jones Quick as a flash!

Captain Smith In the twinkle of an eye!

Captain Jones Neat and tidy.

Captain Smith Spick and span.

King Harry Because we're the Masked Cleaning Ladies of Om.

They go. ***Mary*** *and* ***Jane*** *look at each other. They are still surprised by what's happened.*

Mary I wonder where they came from?

Jane Some place called Om, I suppose. Wherever that is. Have you ever heard of it?

Mary No.

Jane And have you ever heard of cleaning ladies wearing masks before?

Mary No, I haven't.

Jane Nor have I. But I know who *does* wear masks.

Mary Who?

Jane Burglars.

Mary They can't be burglars!

Jane Why not?

Mary They were wearing dresses.

Jane That might just be part of their disguise. Mum told me not to let in any burglars, and perhaps I have.

Mary They might not be. They might just be who they say they are.

Jane There's only one way to find out. We'll have to get them to take their masks off.

Mary And what if they won't?

Jane Then we'll have to unmask them ourselves.

Scene 5

***Captain Jones**, **Captain Smith** and **King Harry** enter, with the dustpan and brush, mop, and vacuum cleaner. They sweep, and mop, and hoover. **Jane** and **Mary** creep in after them, to watch.*

Captain Jones Oh, how I love to see a newly swept floor!

Captain Smith How I love the smell of soapy water in a bucket!

Captain Jones The hiss of the bristles!

Captain Smith The slosh of the mop!

Captain Jones I love cleaning so much –

Captain Smith I just hate to stop!

King Harry *switches off the vacuum cleaner.*

King Harry But we have to, because we've finished.
There! It's all done.

Jane *and* ***Mary*** *come towards King Harry and the Captains.*

Mary *(To Captain Jones)* You were very quick.

Captain Jones We know.

Captain Smith We are.

King Harry The Masked Cleaning Ladies of Om
are famous for their speed.

Jane Now that you've finished, and the castle is clean,
you can take off your masks.

Captain Jones	*(Shocked)* What did you say?
Captain Smith	Take off our masks?
Jane	Yes.
Captain Jones	We can't do that.
Captain Smith	Not at all.
Mary	Why not?
Captain Jones	Because...

Captain Smith Because...

King Harry Because if we do take our masks off, we won't be the Masked Cleaning Ladies of Om!

Jane I see. Oh, well. Never mind.
Can you come again next week?

King Harry Of course we can. Next week, and every week.
We'll be here.

Captain Jones To sweep and polish.

Captain Smith Mop and scrub.

King Harry The Masked Cleaning Ladies of Om!

Captain Jones Here's your dustpan and brush.

***Captain Jones** puts them down.*

Captain Smith Here's your mop and bucket.

***Captain Smith** gives the mop and bucket to Mary.*

King Harry And here's your vacuum cleaner.

King Harry *gives the vacuum cleaner to Jane.*

King Harry Goodbye, then. See you next week.

They start to go.

Jane Not so fast!

Jane *points the vacuum cleaner at them.*

Mary Hold it!

Mary *points the mop at them.*

King Harry What are you doing?

Jane You're not going anywhere!

Captain Jones But we have to!

Captain Smith Let us go!

Jane Not until you take off your masks!

Captain Jones We can't.

Captain Smith It's against the law.

Mary What law?

King Harry The law of Om.

Jane I don't believe you. Take off your masks.
Or I'll suck you into the vacuum.

Mary Slosh you with this mop.

Jane Come on. Take them off!

King Harry All right. You win. All together, ladies.

The three take off their masks.
***Jane** and **Mary** gasp with surprise*
when they see who it is.

Jane Father!

Mary Captain Jones! Captain Smith!

Captain Jones *and* ***Captain Smith*** *speak together.*

Captain Jones
Captain Smith } Hello.

Jane I think you'd better explain.

King Harry Well, my dear, we set off on our quest, and when we reached the woods, we saw a dragon.

Captain Jones We *think* we saw a dragon.

Captain Smith We heard something moving in the woods, and it *sounded* like a dragon.

King Harry A terrible beast!

Captain Jones	A fearsome monster!
Captain Smith	At least, we thought it might be.
King Harry	So we came back home.
Captain Jones	And we dressed up as cleaners.
Captain Smith	We like cleaning much better than fighting dragons.
King Harry	It's a lot safer.

Captain Jones Less dangerous.

Captain Smith And dragons are very rare.
It's not really fair to hunt them.

Jane But you've been telling lies! And you always
told me to tell the truth, Father.

King Harry	I know. And I am very sorry.
Mary	What will the Queen say when she finds out?

Captain Jones *and* ***Captain Smith*** *speak together, scared.*

Captain Jones **Captain Smith**	The Queen!
Jane	*(To Mary)* She won't be very happy when she discovers they haven't found any cleaners or fought any dragons.
Mary	*(To Jane)* She'll probably send them on a year's dragon quest.
King Harry	Don't tell your mother, my dear.
Captain Jones	You wouldn't want us to go away for a whole year, would you?
Captain Smith	And perhaps not ever come back?
King Harry	Please, Jane. Don't tell her.

__Jane__ thinks for a moment.

Jane What do you think I should do, Mary?

Mary Come over here. I've just had an idea.

__Mary__ and __Jane__ whisper together.
Then __Mary__ speaks aloud to Jane.

Mary Well? What do you think?

Jane It's a brilliant idea!

__Jane__ turns to King Harry.

Jane All right. I won't tell Mum. If –

King Harry If what?

Jane If Mary, and all my other friends can come round and play.

King Harry Is that all? Of course.

Jane We're all agreed, then?

__Captain Jones, Captain Smith,__
and __King Harry__ speak together.

Captain Jones **Captain Smith** **King Harry**	Agreed!
Jane	Then let's all go and have tea and cakes to seal our bargain.
Captain Jones	Excellent! My throat's dry from all that sweeping.
Captain Smith	All that mopping's made my stomach rumble.
King Harry	Tea and cakes it is!

They all go.

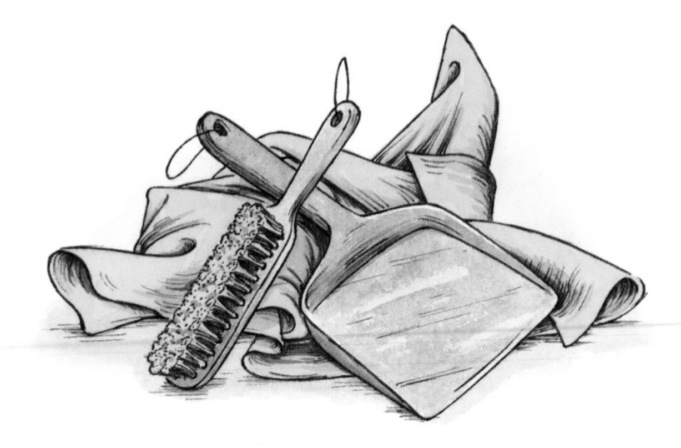

Scene 6

***Queen Norah** enters. She calls out.*

Queen Norah Hello, everyone! I'm back! King Harry! Princess Jane! I'm –

She stops and suddenly notices that the castle is tidy.

Queen Norah Goodness me! The castle! It's been cleaned! And it's been cleaned very well! Not a speck of dust anywhere!

***King Harry**, **Captain Jones**, and **Captain Smith** enter.*

King Harry Hello, dear. Did you have a good tour?

Queen Norah Yes. And I see you've found a cleaner.

Captain Jones Not one cleaner, Your Majesty.

Captain Smith Three cleaners.

Queen Norah Three?

King Harry And they wear masks.

Queen Norah I don't care what they wear. I've never seen the castle looking so neat and tidy. Where did you find them?

Captain Jones Om.

Queen Norah Om?

Captain Smith The city of Om.

Queen Norah I see. Are they here at the moment?

King Harry No. They can only come on Mondays.

Queen Norah Why's that?

Jane enters.

Jane	They're having a lot of trouble with dragons. So Father and the captains are going to fight the dragons on Mondays while the cleaners come and tidy up the castle.
Queen Norah	Harry. You have done well. I'm very proud of you.
King Harry	Thank you, my dear.

__Jane__ gives King Harry a little push.

King Harry Ah, yes! Now that we have proper cleaner, don't you think Jane's friends can come to play again?

Queen Norah Why not? Of course they can.

__Mary__ enters.

Mary Thank you, Queen Norah.

Queen Norah I see there's one of them here already.

Jane I asked her to come round. I was sure you wouldn't mind, now that we've got some cleaners.

Queen Norah No, I don't mind. I'm just happy to see the castle looking so clean.

King Harry And it will be clean from now on.

Jane Because next week, they'll be here again.

Mary Next week, and every week.

Captain Jones	To sweep and polish.
Captain Smith	Mop and scrub.
	All speak together.
All	The Masked Cleaning Ladies of Om!

THE END

Treetops Playscripts
Titles in the series include:

Stage 10
The Masked Cleaning Ladies of Om
by John Coldwell; adapted
by David Calcutt
single: 0 19 918780 0
pack of 6: 0 19 918781 9

Stupid Trousers
by Susan Gates; adapted by David Calcutt
single: 0 19 918782 7
pack of 6: 0 19 918783 5

Stage 11
Bertha's Secret Battle
by John Coldwell; adapted
by David Calcutt
single: 0 19 918786 X
pack of 6: 0 19 918787 8

Bertie Wiggins' Amazing Ears
by David Cox and Erica James; adapted
by David Calcutt
single: 0 19 918784 3
pack of 6: 0 19 918785 1

Stage 12
The Lie Detector
by Susan Gates; adapted by David Calcutt
single: 0 19 918788 6
pack of 6: 0 19 918789 4

Blue Shoes
by Angela Bull; adapted by David Calcutt
single: 0 19 918790 8
pack of 6: 0 19 918791 6

Stage 13
The Personality Potion
by Alan MacDonald; adapted
by David Calcutt
single: 0 19 918792 4
pack of 6: 0 19 918793 2

Spooky!
by Michaela Morgan; adapted
by David Calcutt
single: 0 19 918794 0
pack of 6: 0 19 918795 9

Stage 14
Petey
by Paul Shipton; adapted
by David Calcutt
single: 0 19 918796 7
pack of 6: 0 19 918797 5

Climbing in the Dark
adapted from his own novel
by Nick Warburton
single: 0 19 918798 3
pack of 6: 0 19 918799 1